PAL JOEY

Music by
RICHARD RODGERS

Lyrics by
LORENZ HART

Book by
JOHN O'HARA

Vocal Score
$25.00

Piano Reduction by
ROBERT NOELTNER

Applications for professional and amateur performance of this dramatico-musical should be addressed to the Rodgers & Hammerstein Library, 598 Madison Avenue, New York, N.Y. 10022.

CHAPPELL & CO., INC.

PAL JOEY

Original Production

Presented by GEORGE ABBOTT

December 25, 1940 at the Ethel Barrymore Theatre, New York City

Dances directed by ROBERT ALTON
Scenery and lighting by JO MIELZINER
Costumes by JOHN KOENIG
Production staged by GEORGE ABBOTT
Orchestrations by HANS SPIALEK
Orchestra directed by HARRY LEVANT

Cast of Characters

JOEY EVANS	Gene Kelly
MIKE SPEARS	Robert J. Mulligan
THE KID	Sondra Barrett
GLADYS	June Havoc
AGNES	Diane Sinclair
LINDA ENGLISH	Leila Ernst
VALERIE	Amarilla Morris
ALBERT DOANE	Stanley Donen
VERA SIMPSON	Vivienne Segal
ESCORT	Edison Rice
TERRY	Jane Fraser
VICTOR	Van Johnson
ERNEST	John Clarke
MAX	Averell Harris
STAGEHAND	Jerry Whyte
THE TENOR	Nelson Rae
MELBA SNYDER	Jean Casto
WAITER	Dummy Spevlin
LUDLOW LOWELL	Jack Durant
COMMISSIONER O'BRIEN	James Lane
ASSISTANT HOTEL MANAGER	Cliff Dunstan
SPECIALTY DANCER	Shirley Paige

DANCING GIRLS: Claire Anderson, Sondra Barrett, Alice Craig, Louise de Forrest, Enez Early, Tilda Getze, Charlene Harkins, Janet Davis, Mildred Law, Amarilla Morris, Olive Nicolson, Mildred Patterson, Dorothy Poplar, Diane Sinclair, Mildred Solly, Jeanne Trybom, Marie Vanneman.

DANCING BOYS: Adrian Anthony, Milton Chisholm, Stanley Donen, Randolph Hughes, Richard Irving, Henning Irgens, Van Johnson, Michael Moore, Albert Ruiz.

PAL JOEY

Revival

Presented by JULE STYNE and LEONARD KEY
in association with Anthony B. Farrell

January 3, 1952 at the Broadhurst Theatre, New York City

Dances and Musical Numbers staged by ROBERT ALTON
Settings by OLIVER SMITH
Costumes by MILES WHITE
Lighting by PEGGY CLARK
Musical Director MAX METH
Special Orchestrations by DON WALKER
Production Associate EMIL KATZKA
Book directed by DAVID ALEXANDER
Entire Production supervised by MR. ALTON

Cast of Characters
(In order of appearance)

MIKE	Jack Waldron
JOEY	Harold Lang
KID	Helen Wood
GLADYS	Helen Gallagher
AGNES	Janyce Ann Wagner
MICKEY	Phyllis Dorne
DIANE	Frances Krell
DOTTIE	Lynn Joelson
SANDRA	Eleanor Boleyn
ADELE	Rita Tanno
FRANCINE	Gloria O'Malley
LINDA	Pat Northrop
VERA	Vivienne Segal
VALERIE	Barbara Nichols
WAITER	George Martin
AMARILLA	Thelma Tadlock
ERNEST	Gordon Peters
VICTOR	Robert Fortier
DELIVERY BOY	Barry Ryan
STAGE MANAGER	Clarke Gordon
LOUIS (The Tenor)	Lewis Bolyard
MELBA	Elaine Stritch
LUDLOW LOWELL	Lionel Stander
O'BRIEN	T. J. Halligan

DANCERS: Eleanor Boleyn, Bonnie Brae, Phyllis Dorne, Eleanor Fairchild, Jean Goodall, Patty Ann Jackson, Lynn Joelson, Helene Keller, Frances Krell, Ina Learner, Ethel Martin, June McCain, Gloria O'Malley, Thelma Tadlock, Rita Tanno, Norma Thornton, Janyce Ann Wagner, Harry Asmus, Hank Brunjes, Peter Holmes, Ray Kyle, George Martin, Buzz Miller, David Neuman, Stanley Simmons, George Vosburgh.

PAL JOEY

Synopsis of Scenes

The Time: In the late 1930's

The Place: Chicago

ACT I

SCENE 1: MIKE'S SOUTH SIDE NIGHT CLUB
A September afternoon

SCENE 2: THE PET SHOP
That evening

SCENE 3: MIKE'S NIGHT CLUB
An evening one month later

SCENE 4: A PHONE BOOTH
VERA'S BOUDOIR
The next afternoon

SCENE 5: MIKE'S NIGHT CLUB
After closing time that evening

SCENE 6: THE TAILOR SHOP
A few days later

SCENE 7: BALLET

ACT II

SCENE 1: CHEZ JOEY
A few weeks later

SCENE 2: JOEY'S APARTMENT
The next morning

SCENE 3: CHEZ JOEY
That afternoon

SCENE 4: JOEY'S APARTMENT
Later that afternoon

SCENE 5: THE PET SHOP
Later that evening

Musical Program

PAL JOEY
Overture

Lyrics by
LORENZ HART

Music by
RICHARD RODGERS

Slowly - In 4

Poco più mosso

Waltz tempo - In 3

Str., W.W.

Moderately - In 2

W.W.

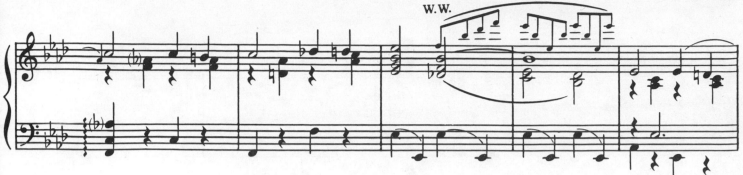

attacca

A Great Big Town
(Opening Act I)

You Mustn't Kick It Around

Cue: JOEY: Now get your places and let's have some co-operation.

Piano

Verse

I have the worst— ap-pre-hen-sion That you don't crave— my at-ten-tion,

But I can't force—you to change your taste._____

If you don't care— to be nice, dear, Then give me air,— but not ice, dear.

Don't let a good — fel - low go to waste. —

For this lit - tle sin that you com - mit at lei - sure,

You'll re - pent in haste. —

A

If my heart gets in your hair, — You must - n't kick it a - round. —

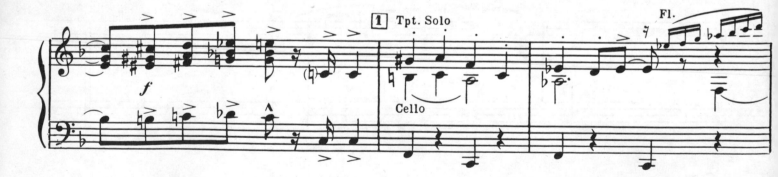

No.2a You Mustn't Kick It Around - Encore

Cue: MIKE: Come on... come on... keep rehearsing.

→ only these 2 pages

You must-n't kick it at all._ When I try to ring the bell_

You nev-er care for the sound._____ The next gal may not do as well,_

You must-n't kick_ it_ a-round.

4 Dance

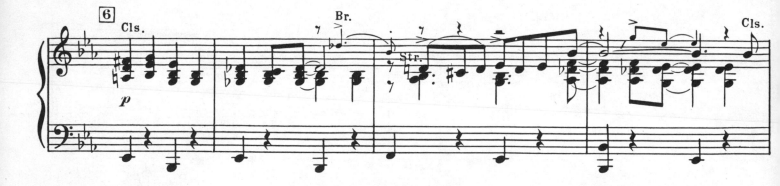

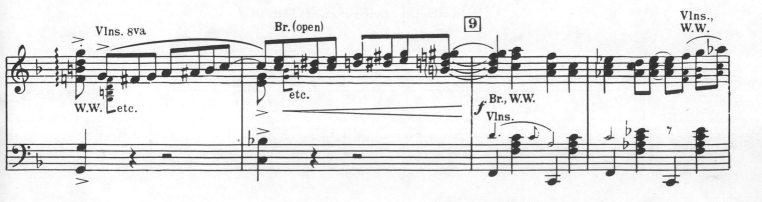

No. 2 aa

Change Of Scene
(You Mustn't Kick It Around)

No. 2b

Opening Scene 2
(Interlude)

Moderately - in 4

Piano

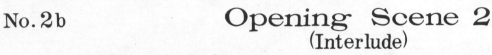

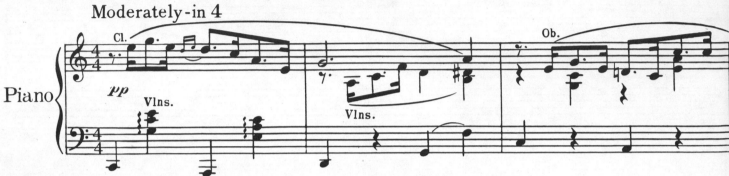

I Could Write A Book

Cue: **JOEY: I didn't mean to bore you with the story of my life.**

But my bus- y mind is burn-ing to use what learn-ing I've got. Fl.

I won't waste an - y time, I'll strike while the i - ron is hot. If they

Hn. Bsn.   Hn., Cello   Cls., Cello

B

asked me I could write a book _____ A - bout the

Vlns.   Vlns.

p (melody)

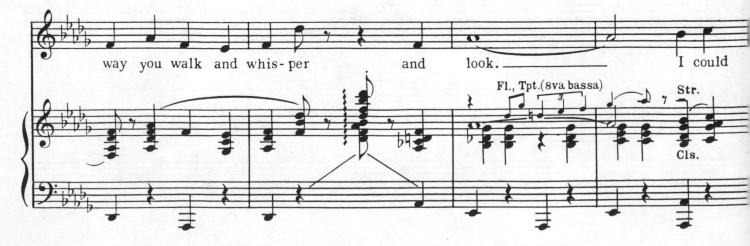

way you walk and whis-per and look. _____ I could

Fl., Tpt.(8va bassa)   Str.

Cls.

write a pre - face on how we met, So the

world would nev - er for - get. _____ And the

sim - ple se - cret of the plot _____ Is just to

tell them that I love you a lot. _____ Then the

E

world dis - cov - ers, as my book ends, How to

make two lov - ers of friends.

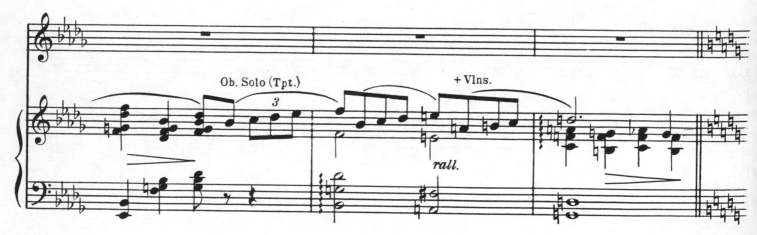

F

LINDA:

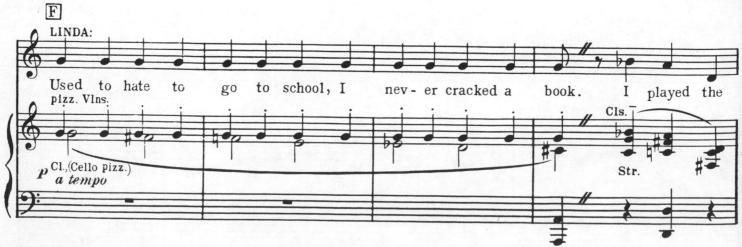

Used to hate to go to school, I nev - er cracked a book. I played the

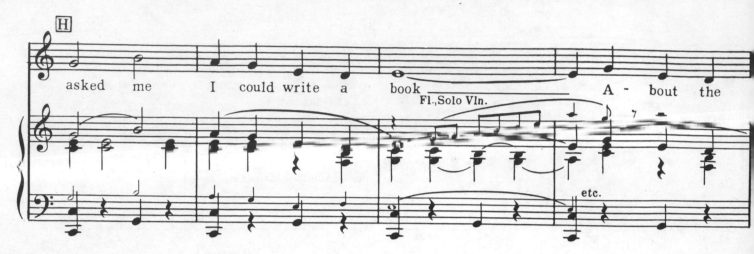

asked me I could write a book _____ A - bout the

Fl.,Solo Vln.

etc.

way you walk and whis - per and look. _____ I could

3

Cl.,Vlns.,Cello

write a pre - face on how we met, So the

Bell
8va

Ob.,Vlns.,Cls.

Hn.

world would nev - er for - get. _____ And the

Vlns.

ff Tutti

B.Cl.,Cello

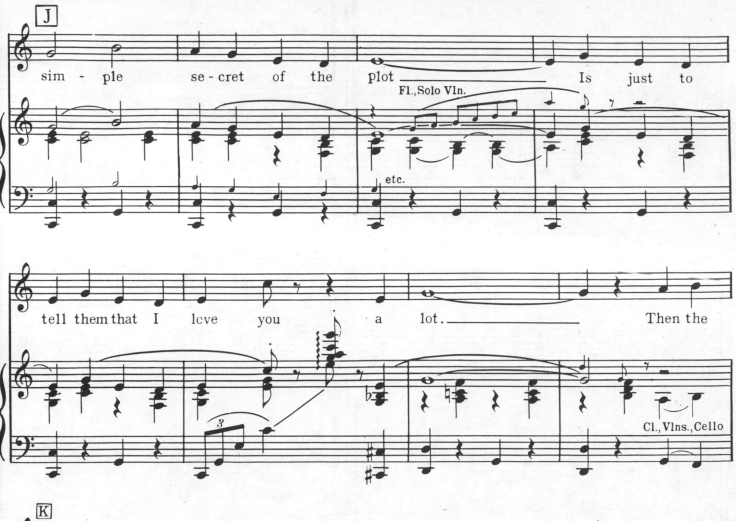

simple se-cret of the plot _____ Is just to

Fl., Solo Vln.

etc.

tell them that I love you a lot. _____ Then the

Cl., Vlns., Cello

world dis - cov - ers, as my book ends, How to

Bell
8va

Vlns.b

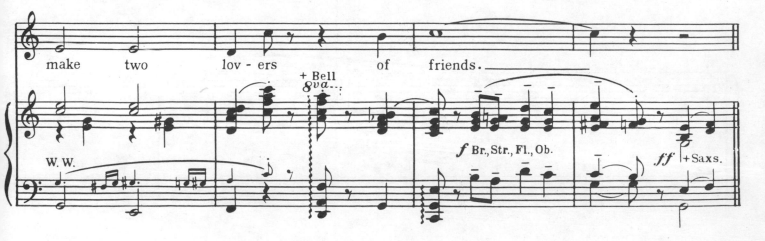

make two lov - ers of friends. _____

+ Bell
8va

W. W.

f Br., Str., Fl., Ob.

ff +Saxs.

Exit
L Poco più mosso

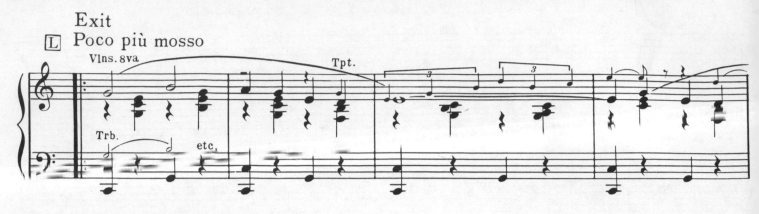

M

Poco meno mosso

A Great Big Town – Reprise
(Opening Scene 3)

Bos - ton is Eng - land, N'Or - leans is France.

New York is an - y - one's for ten cents a dance. __ But this

great big town __ On that great big lake __ Is A -

mer - i - ca's first, __ And A - mer - i - cans make __ Chi -

ca - go. Hi - ya, boys? There's a

great big town __ On a great big lake __ Called Chi -

ca - go. _____ When the

sun goes down __ It is wide a - wake, __ Take your

ma and your pa down to Chi - ca - go. _____ *Saxs.,Vlns.*

6 Bos - ton is Eng - land, N'Or - leans is France.

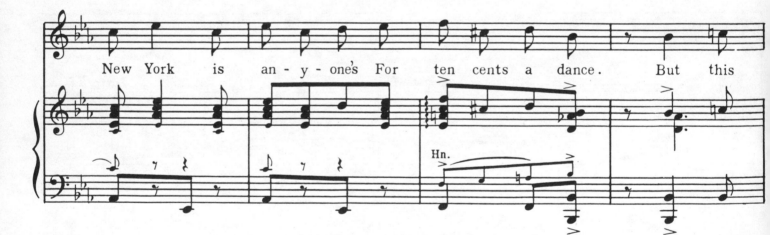

New York is an - y - one's For ten cents a dance. But this

great big town ___ On that great big lake ___ Is A -

mer - i - ca's first, ___ And A - mer - i - cans make ___ Chi -

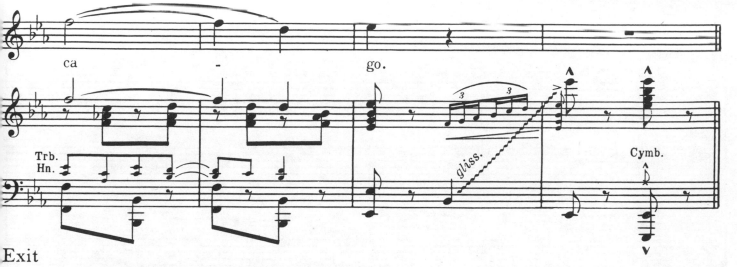

ca - go.

Trb.
Hn.

gliss.

Cymb.

Exit

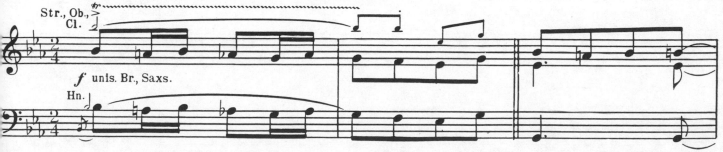

Str., Ob., *tr*
Cl.

f unis. Br, Saxs.

Hn.

gliss.

Cymb.

No. 5

That Terrific Rainbow

Cue: JOEY: .... if I have nothing to tell I'm gonna make it good!

Brass Fanfare-ad lib.

MIKE: Ladies and gentlemen ---- Okay, bring on the girls!

red- hot ma - ma,   But I'm blue __ for you.   I get

pur-ple with an-ger   At the things_ you   do._____ And I'm

green with en - vy   When you meet _ a   dame. _____ But you

burn my heart up   With an or - ange   flame. _____   I'm a

red-hot ma-ma, But you're white _ and cold. _ Don't you

know your ma-ma Has a heart _ of gold? _ Though we're

in those grey clouds, _ Some day _ you'll spy _ That ter-

rif-ic rain-bow O - ver you and I. _

GLADYS and GIRLS:

I'm a   I.

Though we're in those grey clouds ____ Some

day ____ you'll spy ____ 'That ter-rif-ic rain-bow

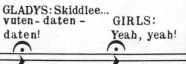

GLADYS: Skiddlee...
vuten-daten-
daten!

GIRLS:
Yeah, yeah!

O-ver you and I. _____

Coda (VICTOR enters)
Tpt. Solo

No. 5a   That Terrific Rainbow – Encore

GIRLS:

Though we're in those grey clouds _____ Some

day _ you'll spy _ That ter-rif-ic rain-bow O - ver you and

GLADYS: I'm a red-hot mama.

GIRLS: Oh skiddle dee boo --- yeah!

Oh, dad - dee - oh - dee - ad - dee, Dad - dee do.

What Is A Man?

Cue: **JOEY:** I just thought I'd tell you to go to h___before I leave.

man? Is he an an - i - mal? Is he a wolf,

Is he a mouse? Is he the cheap or the dear kind? ___

___ Is he cham - pagne or the beer kind? ___

What is a man? Is he a stim - u - lant? Good for the

heart, Bad for the nerves? Na - ture's mis - take since the

world be - gan? What makes me give, What makes me

live? What is this thing called man?

Patter (*briskly*)

VERA:

Hel - lo,

Jack, Can't keep the ap - point - ment. Have an aw - ful

cold. *(Sneeze)*

Hel - lo, Frank, Have to meet my hus - band.

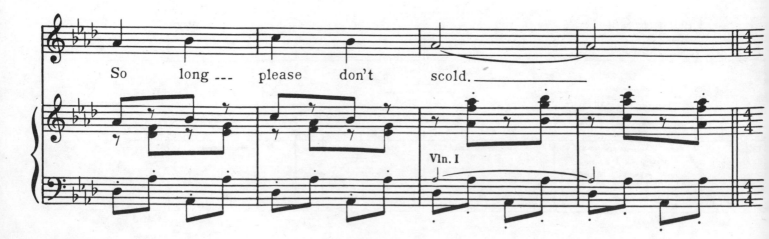

So long --- please don't scold. _____

Hel - lo,   hel - lo,   love. _____

What is a man?   Is he an or - na - ment, Use - less by

day,   Hand - y by night?   Na - ture's mis - take   since the

world be - gan?   They're all a - like,   They're all a -

like. What is this thing called man?

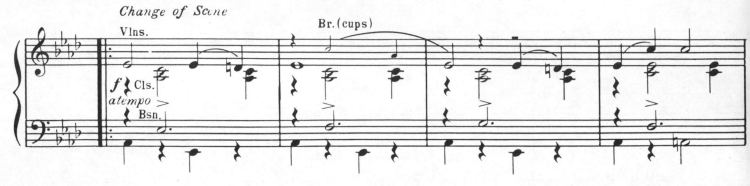

Change of Scene

Vlns.

Br.(cups)

Fade as

curtain rises.

Happy Hunting Horn

ue: DOTTIE: Joey, are you leaving?

Moderato, quasi marciale - In 4

JOEY: E.H. 8 bassa

Don't wor-ry, girls, I'm on-ly on va-ca-tion, Not out of cir-cu-la-tion.

Piano

Vlns. muted
mp Cello, Bass pizz.

Don't wor-ry, girls. +Br. Don't wor-ry, girls, While I still have my eye-sight, You're

going to be in my sight, Don't wor - ry girls. You nev - er can e -

W.W.
Vlns.

♩ = ♩ In 2

rase the hunt-er from the chase.

Vlns.
Br. (cups)

E.H.
W.W. *mf*

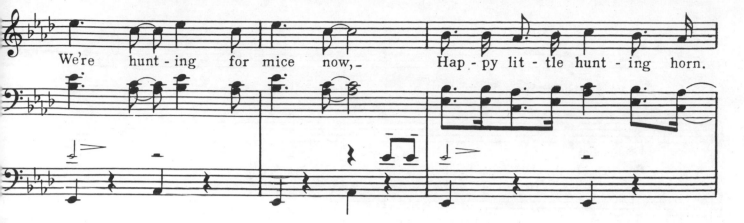

We're hunt-ing for mice now,_ Hap-py lit-tle hunt-ing horn.

2

Dan-ger's eas-y to en-dure When

you're out to catch a beaut._ Lie in am-bush

but be sure When you see the whites of their eyes, Don't shoot!

Play the horn from night to morn, Just play, no — mat - ter

what time. _ Play "There'll be a hot time,"

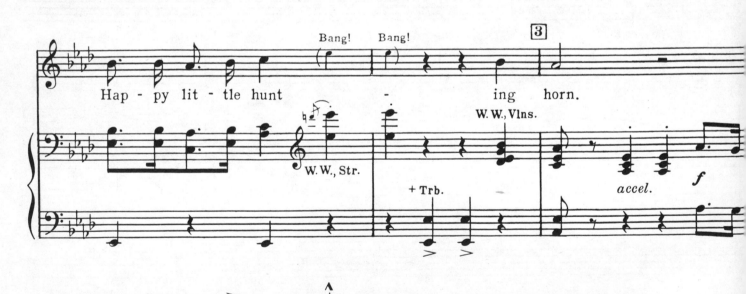

Hap - py lit - tle hunt - ing horn.

Dance

4 A little faster

(Rhythm as before)

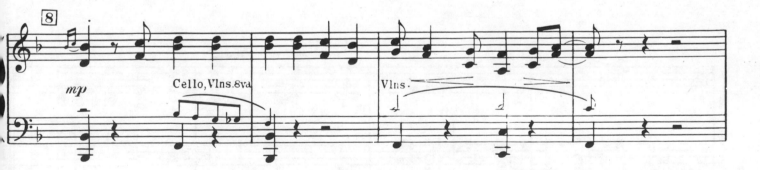

Segue

No. 7a   Happy Hunting Horn – Encore

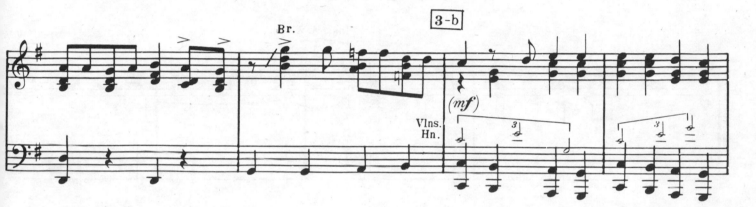

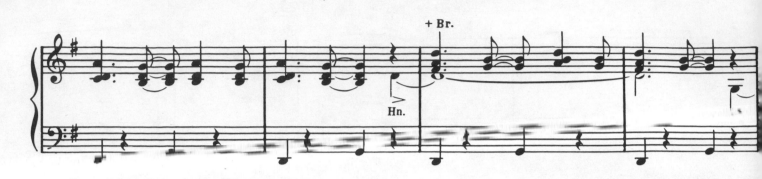

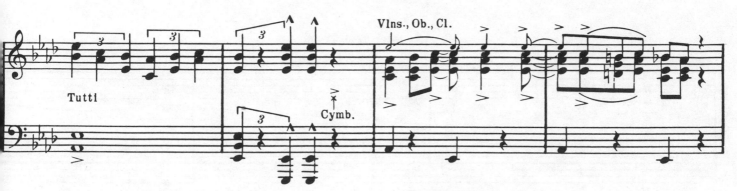

Segue

Change Of Scene
(Happy Hunting Horn)

Bewitched

Cue: JOEY: Well, it got results.

VERA: He's a fool and don't I know it. But a fool can have his charms.

I'm in love and don't I show it, Like a babe in arms.

Love's the same old sad sen-sa-tion. Late-ly I've not slept a wink

love it — Be - cause the laugh's on me. A
speak - ing, — He's at his ver - y best. I'm
clos - er — Than Roe - buck is to Sears.

41

pill he is, But still he is All wine and I'll keep him un -
Vexed a - gain, Per - plexed a - gain, Thank God I can be o - ver -
dumb a - gain And numb a - gain, A rich, read - y, ripe lit - tle

til he is Be - witched, both - ered and be - wil - dered like
sexed a - gain. Be - witched, both - ered and be - wil - dered am
plum a - gain. Be - witched, both - ered and be - wil - dered am

JOEY and ERNEST enter
and look at sample.

VERA: You know

1. 2.   **3.**

me.

Encore

No. 8a

Pal Joey
(What Do I Care For A Dame?)

And I'll be in with the cops.

2 What do I care for the skirts?

What do I care for the skirts?

I'll make them pay till it hurts.

Let them put up till it hurts.

3 I'm going to own a night club,

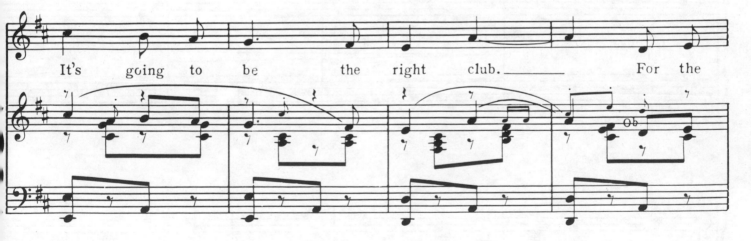

It's going to be the right club. _____ For the

4 swell gen - try, It's el - e - men - ta - ry I'll

wear top hat and cane   In Chez Jo - ey.   They'll pay

Tutti

Jo - ey,   The gay Jo - ey...   I can see it plain.

Alto Solo

Vlns.

pp   poco   rall.   W.W.   Hn.

a tempo

+Tpts.

ff   Trb., Bsn., Cello   + Alto   + Hn.   Br.   f

(Traveler opens)

5   Vlns.   etc.

Alto

Ballet

L'istesso tempo

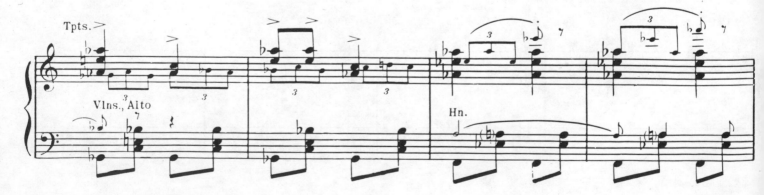

Wah-wah Tpt., Alto, Ob.

+ Fl. 8va

11

Fl., Ob.

(St. mutes) Tpts. 2,3

Trb.

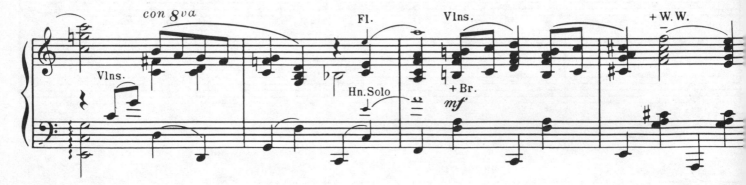

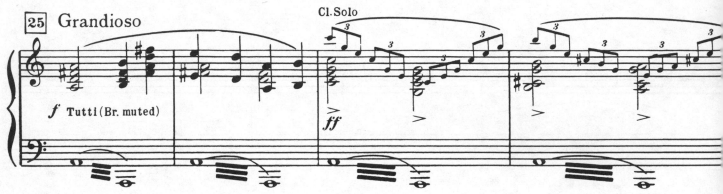

DANCERS:

And the

Vlns. (con 8va)
Clo.
Vla. 3
Bsn., Cello

sim - ple   se - cret of the plot _____ Is just to

(tr continues)

p sempre

tell you that I love you   a   lot. _____   Then the

+Ob.   Br., Bells, Fl.   Br., Str.

Cl., Cello

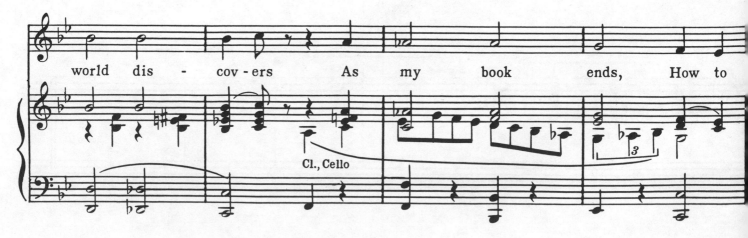

world dis - cov - ers As my book ends,   How to

make two lov-ers of friends.

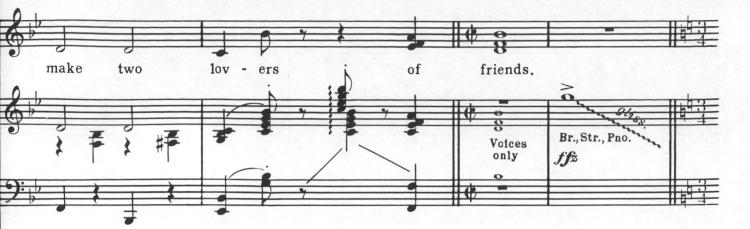

Voices
only

Br., Str., Pno.
ffz

32 Vivo

ff Vlns.

Br.

Saxs. *rall.*

Pno. Flutter

(simile)

33 Vlns. unis.(8va)

ff Tutti

Saxs.

(Vlns.)

Vlns.(Ob. 8 bassa)

mp
Trb., Saxs.,Cello,Hn.

End of Act I

Entr'acte

No. 10 The Flower Garden Of My Heart

Cue: **VICTOR:** All right, Louis, on the bench.

Moderato

Piano

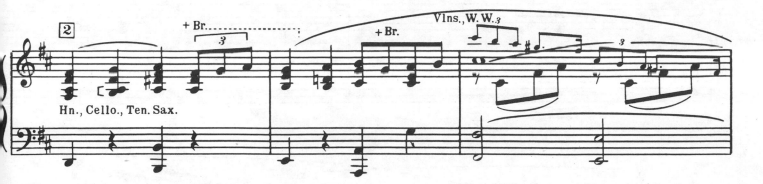

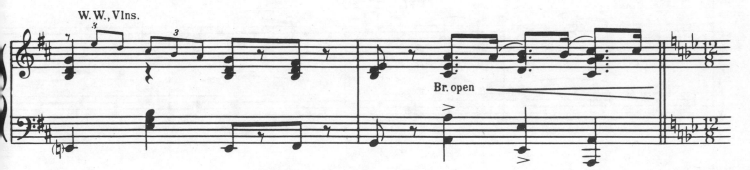

4 Moderato

LOUIS:

I have-n't got a great big yacht, But I'm con-tent-ed with my lot.

I've got one thing much more beau-ti-ful and grand.

I do not own a rac-ing horse, But that don't fill me with re-morse.

I pos-sess the fin-est show-place in the land. _____ So come with

me and wan-der to a love-ly spot out yon-der. In the

5 flow-er gar-den of my heart _____ I've got

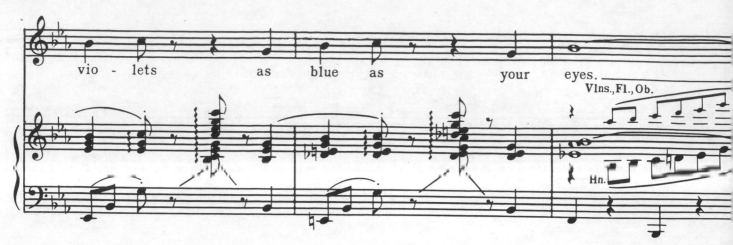

vio - lets   as blue as   your   eyes.

6 I've got dain - ty nar - cis - sus as sweet as my

mis - sus And lil - ies as pure as the skies.

7 In the flow - er gar - den of my heart

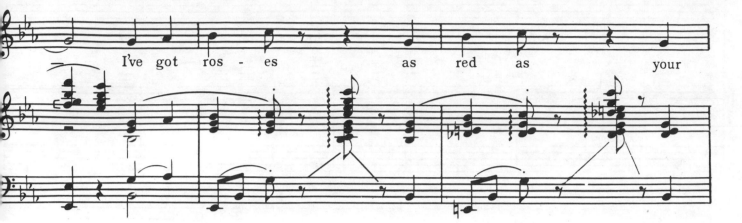

I've got ros - es as red as your

8

mouth. _____ Just to keep our love ho - ly I've

Vlns., Fl., Ob.

Str.

Hn.   Hn.

got glad - i - o - li And sun-flow - ers fresh from the

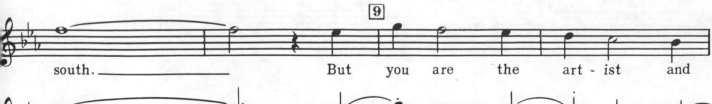

9

south. _____ But you are the art - ist and

mf

Br.   Tutti

flow - er gar - den of my heart _____ I've got

dais-ies to tell you you're true.___ Oh, the

west-wind will whisk us the scent of hi-bis-cus And

heath-er that's smoth-ered with dew._____ In the

flow-er gar-den of my heart_____ I've got

li - lacs and dain - ty sweet peas. _____ You will

etc.   Br.   + Br.

look like sweet wil - liam And smell like a tril - lium Sur -

Cls.   etc.   etc.

round - ed by fond bum - ble bees. _____ But

Vlns.

Br.   Br.

you are the pas - try And I am the tart, In the

Fl., Cl.

Vlns.
8va

etc.

flow - er gar - den of my heart. _____

22 Fl., Ob., Vlns.

Dance

Str.

Fl.

Tutti

Br., Saxs.

Str.

subito

Fl.. (Ob. 8 bassa)

+ W. W., Saxs.

no Saxs.

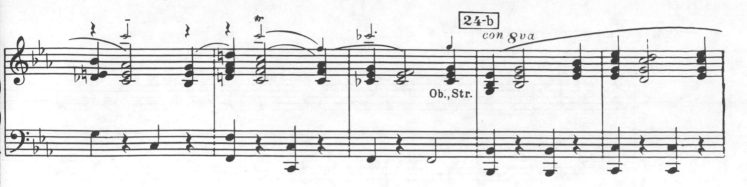

Zip

Cue: MICHAEL: Like for instance?

Moderately

MELBA:

I've in-ter-viewed Pab-lo Pi-

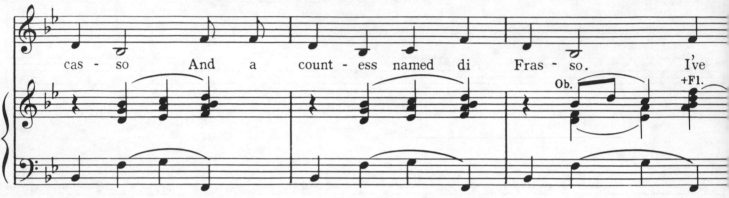

cas-so And a count-ess named di Fras-so. I've

in-ter-viewed the great Stra-vin-sky. But my great-est a-chieve-ment is the

in-ter-view I had with the star who worked for Min-ski.

I met her at the Yank-ee Clip - per And she

did - n't un - zip one zip - per. I said "Miss Lee, you are

such an art - ist, Tell me why you nev - er miss."

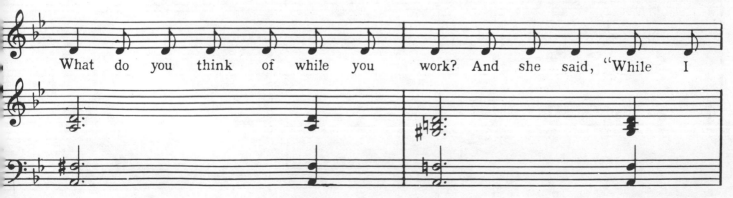

What do you think of while you work? And she said, "While I

work my thoughts go some-thing like this:

Refrain

Zip! Walt - er Lipp - man was - n't bril - liant to - day.
Zip! I con - sid - er Dal - i's paint - ing pas - sé.
Zip! Tos - ca - ni - ni leads the great - est of bands.

Str., W.W.

Zip! Will Sar - oy - an ev - er
Zip! Can they make the Met - ro -
Zip! Jer - gens Lo - tion does the

write a great play?__ Zip! I was
pol - i - tan pay?__ Zip! En - glish
trick for his hands.__ Zip! Rip Van

Or a man who's voice is al - to. Zip! I'm a het - ero - sex - ual.
Char - lie's aunt, or Shu - bert's bro - ther. Zip! I'm mis - o - gyn - is - tic.
Mouse and Roon - ey make me sick - y! Zip! I'm a lit - tle hec - tic.

Zip! It took in - tel - lect to mas - ter my art.
Zip! My in - tel - li - gence is guid - ing my hand.
Zip! My ar - tis - tic taste is clas - sic and dear.

Zip! Who the hell is Mar - gie Hart?
Zip! Who the hell is Sal - ly Rand?
Zip! Who the hell is Li - li St.

1. 2.

3.

Cyr?

VICTOR enters

No. 12 Plant You Now, Dig You Later

Cue: MICHAEL: Go ahead and rehearse.

Moderato - In 2

GLADYS: Sweet-heart, the day is wan-ing, Must go with-out com-plain-ing. Time for Auf Wie-der-sehn-ing now.

Don't let this sad dis-clos-ure Ruf-fle your calm com-pos-ure. Smile at the one who knows your ev-'ry

whim. Wait for him now. Where's the

A

check? Get me the wait - er I'm not going to

stay. Plant you now Dig you lat - er, I'm

on my way. My re - gret could - n't be

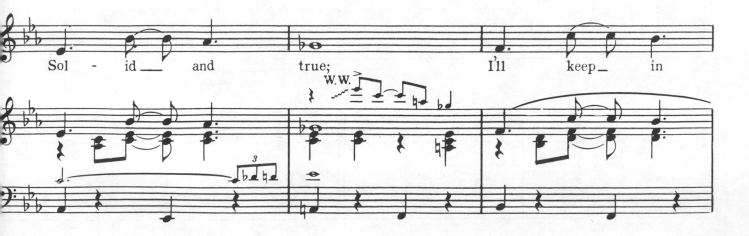

step, chick, Till I come dig - ging for you.

Br., Cymb.   Fl.   + B.D.   + B.D.

So, lit - tle po - tat - er,— Stay right where you are.— Plant you

Pa., 2 Fls.   Vlns.   Str.   W.W.

now— Dig you lat - er— Means `au re - voir,— just au re-

+ W.W.

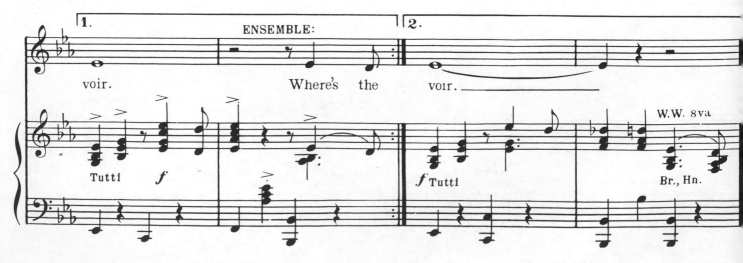

1.   ENSEMBLE: 2.

voir.   Where's the   voir.—

Tutti   f   f Tutti   W.W. 8va   Br., Hn.

B-3

C Coda
Vlns., W.W.

Dance

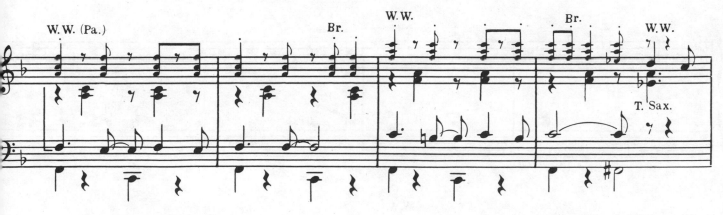

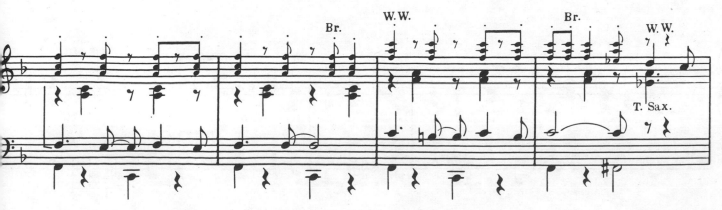

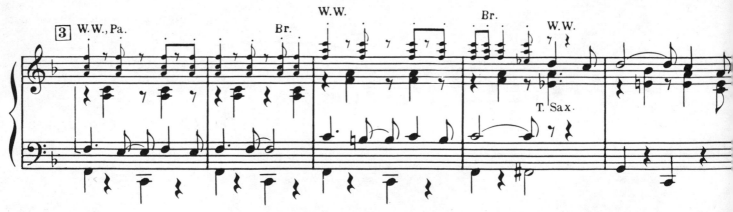

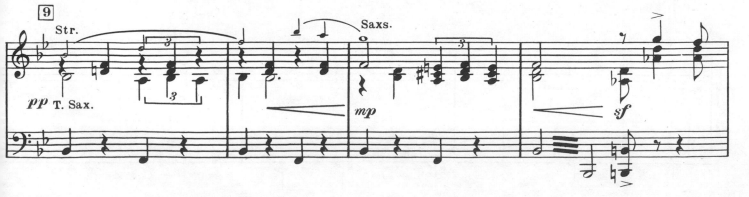

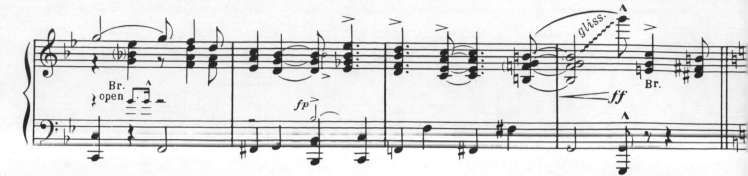

attacca

Plant You Now, Dig You Later - Encore

No. 12a

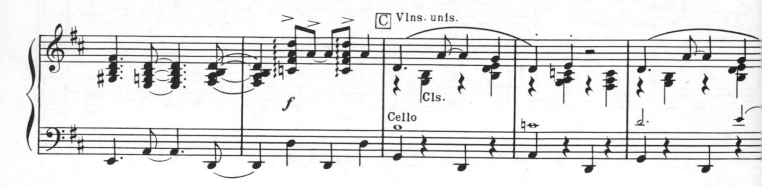

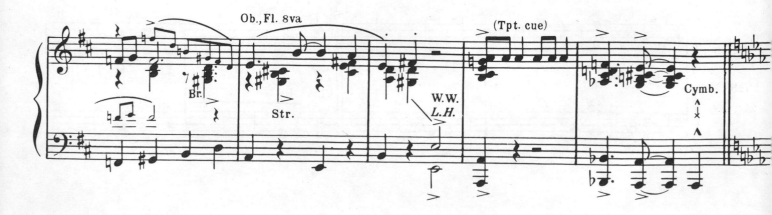

For Change Of Scene - repeat Encore as needed

No. 13 Den Of Iniquity

Cue: JOEY: Terrible apartment? Why, this is the <u>nuts</u>.
VERA: Yes, dear.

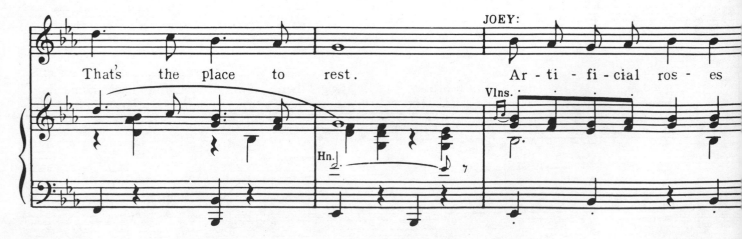

'round the door, They are nev-er out of bloom;

VERA:

And a flow-ered car-pet on the floor In the liv - ing room. In our

Vlns. (+ Cls. 8 bassa)

BOTH:

Br. (harmon mutes)

rall.

p

A

lit - tle den of in - iq - ui - ty Our ar - range-ment is
lit - tle den of in - iq - ui - ty For a girl - y and

Vlns.

a tempo Pno. Solo

VERA:

good. It's much more health-y liv - ing here; This rush-ing back home is
boy. (Vera:) We'll sit and let the ho-urs pass; A can - o - py bed has

2 Fls.

Ob.

Str.

bad, my dear. I have-n't caught a cold all year. Knock on
so much class. *(Joey:)* And so's a ceil-ing made of glass, Oh, what

wood! It was ev-er thus, since an-tiq-ui-ty, Down to you and
joy! *(Both:)* Love has been that way, since an-tiq-ui-ty, All the po-ets a-

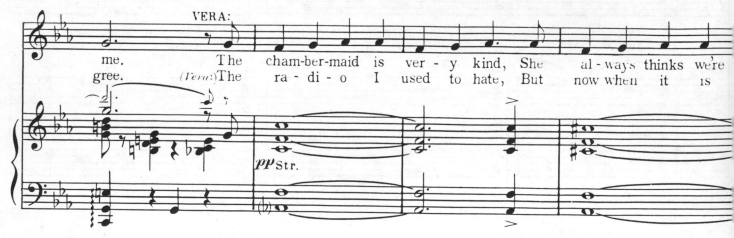

me. The cham-ber-maid is ver-y kind, She al-ways thinks we're
gree. *(Vera:)* The ra-di-o I used to hate, But now when it is

so re-fined... Of course, she's deaf and dumb and blind. No fools
dark and late, Ra-vel's Bo-le-ro works just great. That's for

we___ In our lit-tle den of in-iq-ui-ty.

me (*Both:*) In our lit-tle den of in-iq-ui

Vlns., W.W.

+Cls.

mf Cello

In our ty.___

p

rit.

Ped. *

B Dance

Br.

mf   Vlns.   3

W.W.

muted Tpt., Hn.

Vlns. 8va

Vlns.

Tutti

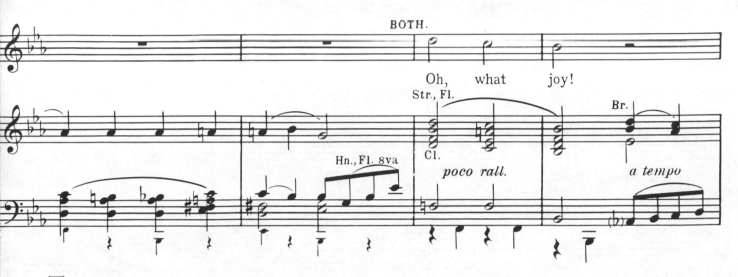

Oh, what joy!

We're

ver - y prop - er folks, you know. We've sep-'rate bed-rooms "comme il faut." There's

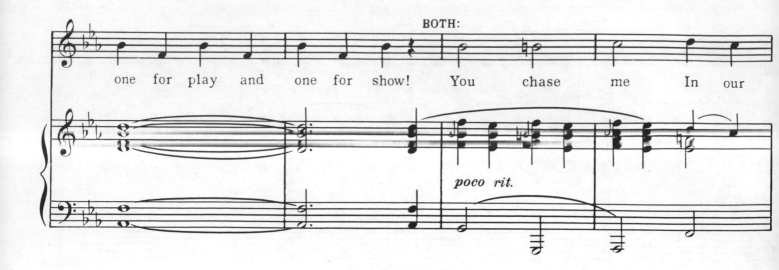

BOTH:

one for play and one for show! You chase me In our

poco rit.

lit - tle den of in - iq - ui - ty.

+Cls.

W.W., Str.

Hn., Cello

Fl., (Cl. 8 bassa)

E

p

etc.

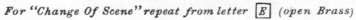

For "Change Of Scene" repeat from letter $\boxed{E}$ *(open Brass)*

No.14   Do It The Hard Way

Cue: **VERA:** You always do everything the hard way.

not re-tard the young Cab Cal-lo-way. Now

3 Moderately

hear him blow _____ his vo-de-o-do _____ to -

day. _____

4

Do it the hard way And it's eas-y sail-ing. _____

Do it the hard way And it's hard to lose._____

5

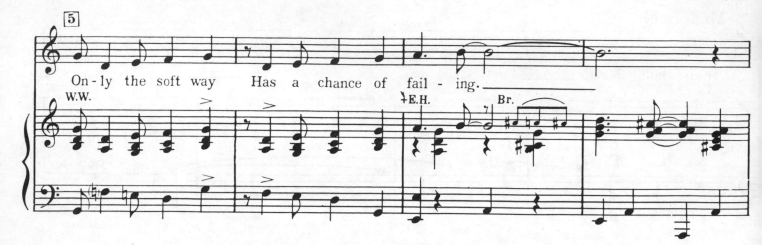

On-ly the soft way Has a chance of fail - ing._____

You have_____ to choose._____

6

I took the hard way When I tried to get you._____

You took the soft way When you said "we'll see?"

7

Dar - ling,— now I'll— let you—

Do it the hard way, Now that you want

1.
me.————

2.
me.————

9 Dance

10

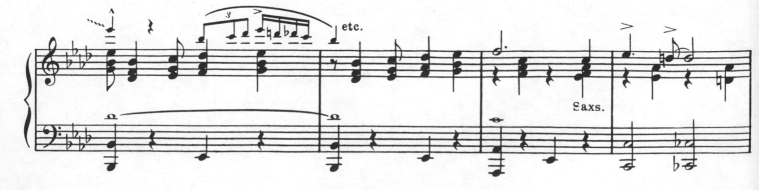

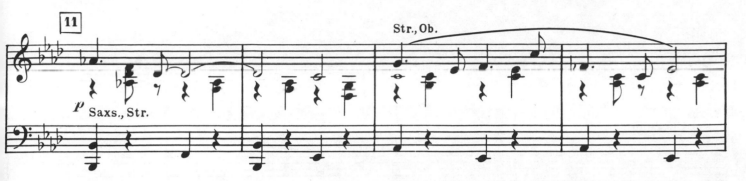

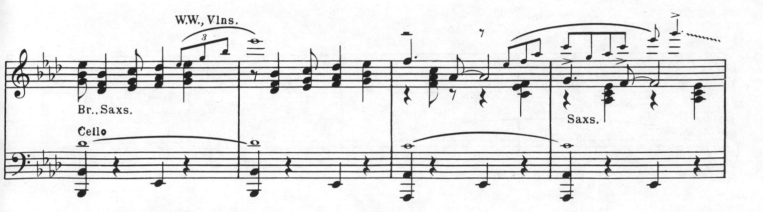

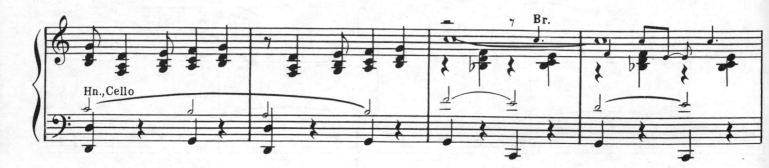

154

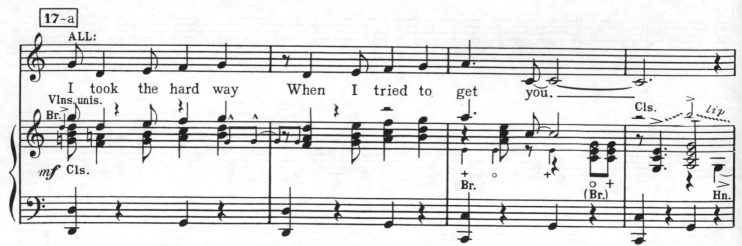

I took the hard way When I tried to get you._____

You took the soft way When you said "We'll see."

Do It The Hard Way - Encore
(Optional)

L'istesso tempo

Piano

Take Him

Cue: LINDA: Well, just don't think it was what you think it was. Take him.

Keep him from fall-ing a - part.
And you'll need as - pi - rin too.

Take him, but don't ev - er take him to
Take him, but don't ev - er let him take

1.
heart.

2.
you.

JOEY: Well, how do you like it?
Dialogue continues.....

Bell

mf Tutti

mf Tutti

arp. ad lib.

at Cue: VERA:...even if we described him to you.

Largo

LINDA and VERA:

I hope that things will go well with him,

1st Vlns.

pizz. Vlns.

mp Str., W.W.

Cls.

p

etc.

I bear no hate.

All I can say is "the hell with him,"

(1st Vlns.)

Cls.

etc.

He gets the gate. So take my ben - e - dic - tion; Take my Old Ben - e - dict too. Take it a - way, it's too good to be true.

No. 15a

Take Him - Dance

attacca

Tempo di Valse

Piano

Coda: Allegretto

attacca

Tango Specialty

Tempo di Tango

Piano

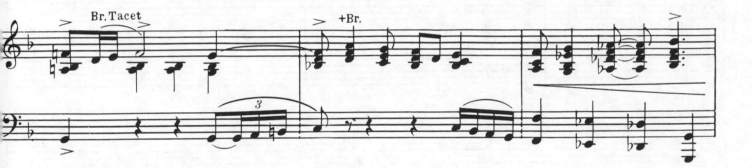

No. 16

Bewitched - Reprise

Cue: JOEY: Blow.
VERA: Yes, dear.

Moderately - In 2

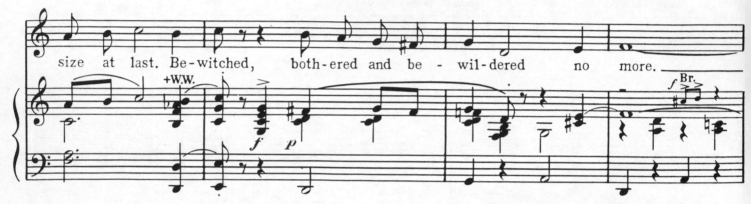

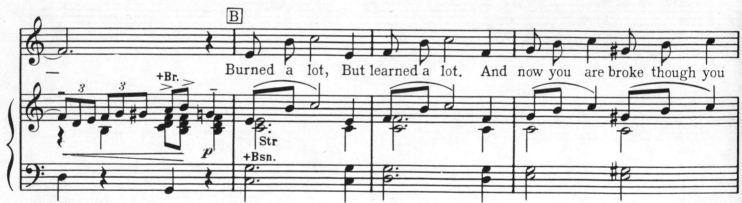

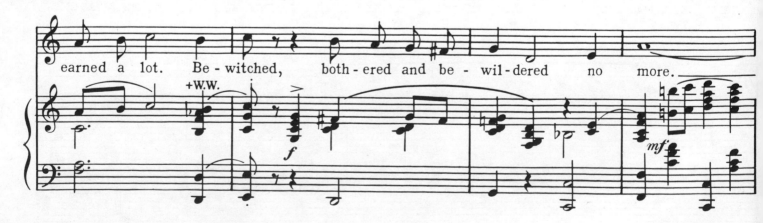

No. 17 Change Of Scene

Finale
(I Could Write A Book)

No.18

Cue: **JOEY: And thanks, thanks a million.**

Moderato commodo - In 2

JOEY.

If they asked me I could write a book __ A - bout the way you walk and whis - per and look. __ I could write a pre - face on how we met, So the world would nev - er for-

get. _____ And the sim - ple se - cret of the

plot _____ Is just to tell them that I love you a

lot. _____ Then the world dis - cov - ers, as

my book ends, How to make two

lov - ers of friends.

2.

friends.

If they

Curtain

attacca

No. 18 a

Curtain Calls
(I Could Write A Book)

Moderato assai

A

Piano

B

attacca

Exit Music

No. 19

Piano

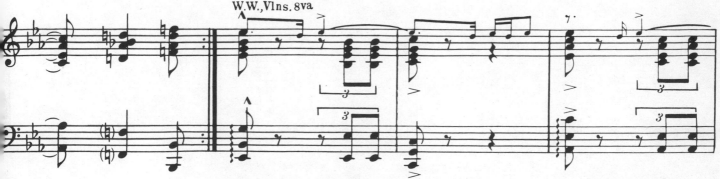